Come Rejoice!

Edited by Michael Perry

Jubilate Hymns
Marshall Pickering : Hope Publishing Company

Marshall Pickering
Middlesex House
34–42 Cleveland Street
London W1P 5FB

Hope Publishing Company
Carol Stream, Illinois 60188, USA

First published 1989
ISBN
Marshall Pickering 0-551-01948-4
Hope Publishing Company 0-916642-38-0
Code No. 899

Typeset in the UK by
Barnes Music Engraving Ltd
East Sussex, England TN22 4HA

Printed in the UK by
Henry Ling Ltd
The Dorset Press, Dorchester

Contents

Preface

The Jubilate group, as it has come to be known, was founded in the early 1960's by Michael Baughen (now Bishop of Chester) and friends closely involved in work among young people. The group pooled their talents to meet the challenge of a new generation who wished to extend their singing beyond the foursquare ways of metrical hymnody, and the unpredictability of Anglican chant!

Initially, no publisher could be found to support the first joint enterprise, *Youth Praise* (1966). The Church Pastoral Aid Society came to the rescue, later publishing *Youth Praise 2* (1969), and *Psalm Praise* (1973) which was a contemporary effort to revitalise the use of Psalms. *Youth Praise* was a best-seller in its time and *Psalm Praise* goes on and on . . .

As the work on *Psalm Praise* got under way, the group comprised Michael Baughen (by this time at All Souls' Church, Langham Place), Richard Bewes (who later succeded him as Rector), Christopher Collins, Timothy Dudley-Smith (who afterwards became Bishop of Thetford), Christopher Idle, Gavin Reid, Edward Shirras, Michael Perry, Michael Saward, James Seddon, Norman Warren, and David Wilson – a mixed bunch of talent, in terms of words and music.

In the mid-1970's an enlarged section of the group under Michael Baughen's leadership (most of whom are represented in this volume) began to apply themselves to the production of a pioneering modern language hymnal[1]. After years of conference and dedication, *Hymns for Today's Church* was born in 1982. *HTC* now sells in six separate editions.

About this time, George Shorney of Hope Publishing in Carol Stream, Illinois, USA, enlisted the cooperation, first of Timothy Dudley-Smith, and then of the extended Jubilate Hymns group. His was a far-sighted move towards mutual enrichment of the USA and UK repertoires[2]. Thus Jubilate and their works have found their way into USA hymnals – *Worship, Rejoice in the Lord, The Hymnal 1982, Psalter Hymnal*, and others. Similarly, American hymns are beginning to emerge in Jubilate publications.

Jubilate authors and musicians – there are now forty of them – differ remarkably in their style, taste and approach. Since the major figures among them are all friends, and can take firm criticism from one another, there is a considerable strength in their working together. Their breadth of style is also reflected in a variety of Jubilate publications: *Church Family Worship* (1986 and 1988), *Carols for Today* (1986), *Carol Praise* (1987), *Let's Praise* (1988), *The Wedding Book* (1989), and *Psalms for Today* and *Songs from the Psalms* (1989–90).

This present collection *Come Rejoice!* illustrates their *hymn* style, and includes some of their most popular combinations of words and music, as well as a cluster of previously unpublished works which the editor believes will be gladly received by the churches. As well as their mutual love of hymnody, Jubilate authors and musicians share a confidence in the future of church music and an energising faith in the Spirit of God who brings life to human offerings of talent and devotion.

[1]See: *Hymns in Today's Language*, Christopher Idle, Grove Books, Bramcote, Nottingham, UK; 1982.

[2]See: *The Hymnal Explosion in North America*, George H Shorney, Hope Publishing Company, Carol Stream, Illinois 60188; 1988.

1 Blow upon the trumpet

1 Blow up-on the trum-pet!
2 Blow up-on the trum-pet!
3 Blow up-on the trum-pet!
4 Blow up-on the trum-pet!

clap your hands to - ge - ther,   sound a - loud the prai - ses of the
let the na-tions trem-ble;   see what power o - bli - ter - ates the
Ar - rows in the light-ning   fly the storm of bat - tle where we
Christ is sure-ly com-ing,   hea - ven's for - ces mo - bil - i - zing

Lord your king.   God has kept the pro - mise, gran-ting us sal -
sun and moon.   This is God's own ar - my bring-ing all to
march a - long.   Glo - ry to our shep - herd keep-ing us through
at his word.   We shall rise to meet him: death at last is

- va - tion: let the peo-ple ju - bil - ant - ly shout and sing!
judge-ment,   for the day of Je-sus Christ is com - ing soon.
dan - ger,   set-ting us like je-wels in a ro - yal crown!
con-quered,   God gives us the vic - to - ry through Christ our Lord!

Words: from Psalm 95, Joel 2 etc., Michael Perry
Music: Norman Warren

Philip James
6 6 11 D

Let God, who called the worlds

```
1 Let    God,   who   called  the   worlds  to   be,   a -
2 This   God    is    ours,   and   yet     we   break the
3 For    though our   lips    have  preached God's law,  our
4 What   then   shall God     the   Lord    de - mand? Not
```

```
- rise  in   all - con - sum - ing   fire  to   judge the peo - ple
  co - ve - nant made  long  a -  go; God's words we   fool - ish -
  err - ing hearts have scorned the Name; we  choose the thief and
  gifts or   lav - ish of -  fer - ing, but vows and  pro - mis -
```

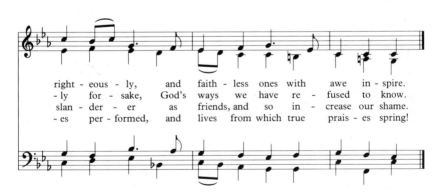

```
  right - eous - ly,  and   faith - less ones with  awe  in - spire.
  - ly    for - sake, God's ways  we    have re -  fused to   know.
  slan -  der - er    as    friends, and so  in -  crease our shame.
  - es    per - formed, and lives from which true  prais - es spring!
```

Alternative tune: Solothurn

Words: from Psalm 50, David Mowbray

Music: English traditional melody, arranged by David Iliff

A babe is born
8 8 8 8 (LM)

3

O people, listen

1 O people, lis-ten—hear God's wis-dom cry-ing! Al-
2 For God will take the ho-ly in-to hea-ven, by
3 To Fa-ther, Son and Spi-rit be the glo-ry! Come,

-though the dark-ness comes to rich and poor, and
grace re-deem the faith-ful from the grave; we
wor-ship and a-dore the ho-ly Name; let

no-thing mor-tal can sur-vive our dy-ing, yet
leave be-hind us all the world has giv-en, and
wis-dom think up-on our hu-man sto-ry, and

in the morn-ing jus-tice shall en-dure:
trust God's migh-ty power to love and save!
faith our ev-er-liv-ing God pro-claim.

Alternative tunes: Highwood, O perfect love (35)

Words: from Psalm 49, Michael Perry
Music: Norman Warren

Wharfdale
11 10 11 10

Now let us learn of Christ

1 Now let us learn of Christ: he speaks, and we shall find
2 Now let us love in Christ as he has first loved us;
3 Now let us grow in Christ and look to things a - bove,
4 Now let us stand in Christ in ev - ery trial we meet,

he light-ens our dark mind; so let us learn of Christ.
as he en - dured the cross, so let us love in Christ.
and speak the truth in love; so let us grow in Christ.
in all his strength com - plete; so let us stand in Christ.

Alternative tune: Quam dilecta

Words: Christopher Idle
Music: M Tiddeman (1837–1915)

Ibstone
6666

Words: © 1980 by Christopher Idle / Jubilate Hymns Ltd; USA © 1980 by Hope Publishing Company, Carol Stream IL 60188

5   Had he not loved us

Unison

mp

1 Had he not
2 Had he not
3 Had he not

Harmony

loved   us   he had   ne - ver come,   yet   is   he   love   and love is
loved   us   he had   ne - ver come;   had   he not   come   he need have
loved   us   he had   ne - ver come;   still were we   lost   in   sor - row,

all   his   way;   low   to   the   mys - tery of the   vir - gin's   womb
ne - ver   died   nor won the   vic - tory of the   va - cant   tomb,
sin and shame,   the doors fast   shut   on   our   e - ter - nal   home

Unison

Christ bows his   glo   -   ry - born   on   Christ - mas   Day.
the   aw - ful   tri   -   umph of the   cru - ci - fied.
which   now stand   o   -   pen - for   he   loved   and   came.

Words: Timothy Dudley-Smith
Music: Peter White

Beacon Hill
10 10 10 10

Jesus, child of Mary

Gently
Descant

4 An - gel hosts the skies a - dorn,

1 Je - sus, child of Ma - ry born,
2 To this place of pain and fear
3 In - fant in a man - ger laid,
4 An - gel hosts the skies a - dorn,

we with shep-herds glo - ri - fy Je - sus, child of

Son of God and Lord most high; come to wear a
love de - scends in hu - man guise; God in Christ self -
wrapped a - bout with pea - sant shawl; gift of grace so
we with shep-herds glo - ri - fy Je - sus, child of

Ma - ry born, Son of God most high.

crown of thorn, brave - ly come to die.
- emp - tied here, fool - ish - ness most wise:
free - ly made, sav - ior for us all.
Ma - ry born, Son of God most high.

Alternative tune: Charity

Words: Michael Perry
Music: Michael Perry, arranged with descant by Norman Warren

Hayle
7775

7 Holy child

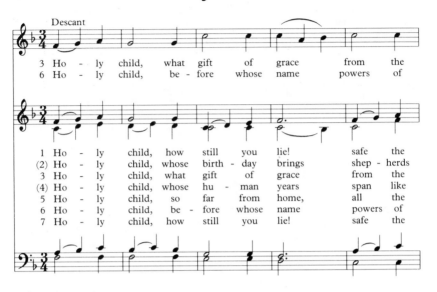

Descant
3 Ho - ly child, what gift of grace from the
6 Ho - ly child, be - fore whose name powers of

1 Ho - ly child, how still you lie! safe the
(2) Ho - ly child, whose birth - day brings shep - herds
3 Ho - ly child, what gift of grace from the
(4) Ho - ly child, whose hu - man years span like
5 Ho - ly child, so far from home, all the
6 Ho - ly child, be - fore whose name powers of
7 Ho - ly child, how still you lie! safe the

Fa - ther free - ly willed! In your in - fant
dark - ness faint and fall; con - quered, death and

man - ger, soft the hay; faint up - on the
from their field and fold, an - gel choirs and
Fa - ther free - ly willed! In your in - fant
ours de - light and pain; one in hu - man
lost to seek and save, to what dread - ful
dark - ness faint and fall; con - quered, death and
man - ger, soft the hay; clear up - on the

Alternative tune: Holy child

Words: Timothy Dudley-Smith
Music: Brian Hoare

Ruxley
7 7 7 7

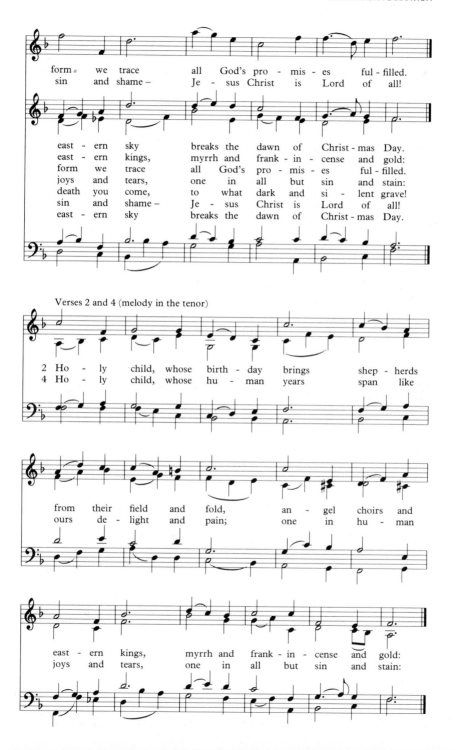

form   we   trace   all   God's pro - mis - es   ful - filled.
sin   and shame –   Je - sus Christ   is   Lord   of   all!

east - ern   sky   breaks the   dawn   of   Christ - mas Day.
east - ern   kings,   myrrh and   frank - in - cense   and gold:
form   we   trace   all   God's   pro - mis - es   ful - filled.
joys   and   tears,   one   in   all   but   sin   and stain:
death   you   come,   to   what   dark   and   si - lent grave!
sin   and   shame –   Je - sus   Christ is   Lord   of   all!
east - ern   sky   breaks the   dawn   of   Christ - mas Day.

Verses 2 and 4 (melody in the tenor)

2 Ho - ly   child, whose   birth - day   brings   shep - herds
4 Ho - ly   child, whose   hu - man   years   span   like

from   their   field   and   fold,   an - gel   choirs   and
ours   de - light   and   pain;   one   in   hu - man

east - ern   kings,   myrrh and   frank - in - cense   and   gold:
joys   and   tears,   one   in   all   but   sin   and stain:

8 When things began to happen

1 When things be-gan to hap-pen, be - fore the birth of time, the
Word was with the Fa - ther and shared his ho - ly name; with-
out him there was no-thing — all life de-rives from him; his
light shines in the dark-ness — an un - ex - tin-guished beam.

2 He came to his cre - a - tion, the work of his own hand; he
en - tered his own coun-try but they would not res - pond: yet
some gave their al - le-giance of life and heart and mind; thus
they be-came his sub-jects and he be - came their friend.

3 Con - ceived by hea-ven's mer-cy, there was no hu-man birth; for
they are God's own child-ren re - deemed from sin and death: and
they be-held his glo - ry, so full of grace and truth; in
Christ, God's Son, our sav - ior, whom we a - dore by faith.

Alternative tune: Ich rede

Words: from John 1, Michael Saward
Music: Norman Warren

The Vines
7 6 7 6 D

All my heart this night rejoices

1 All my heart this night re - joi - ces, as I hear, far and near, sweet-est an - gel voi - ces. 'Christ is born!' their choirs are sing - ing, till the air ev - ery-where now with joy is ring - ing.

2 Lis - ten! from a hum-ble man - ger comes the call, 'One and all, run from sin and dan - ger! Christ-ians come, let no-thing grieve you: you are freed! All you need I will sure - ly give to you.'

3 Ga - ther, then, from ev - ery na - tion; here let all, great and small, kneel in a - dor - a - tion; love him who with love is yearn-ing: Hail the star that from far bright with hope is burn - ing!

4 You, my Lord, with love I'll cher - ish, live to you, and with you dy - ing, shall not per - ish, but shall dwell with you for ev - er: joy di - vine shall be mine that can al - ter ne - ver.

Words: after P Gerhardt (1607–1676), C Winkworth (1826–1878)
Music: David Peacock

All my heart
8336D

10 A child is born for us today

1 A child is born for us to-day, a son to us is given; the sav – ior comes to guide our way and lead us up to heaven. They'll call him 'Won – der-ful', heaven – ly 'Coun – sell – or'.

2 He comes to be the 'Prince of peace', to all the world a friend; his might – y love will ne – ver cease, his king – dom will not end. They'll call him 'Might – y God', 'E – ter – nal Fa – ther'.

3 On those who walk the dark – est way has dawned a shin – ing light far bright – er than the bright – est day, a great and glo – rious sight. O come, Em – man – u – el, our God, be with us!

Words: from Isaiah 9, Pearl Beasley
Music: Brian Hoare

We'll call him Jesus
Irregular

Words: © 1986 by Pearl Beasley / Jubilate Hymns Ltd; USA © 1986 by Hope Publishing Company, Carol Stream IL 60188
Music: © 1986 by Brian Hoare / Jubilate Hymns Ltd; USA © 1986 by Hope Publishing Company, Carol Stream IL 60188

Arrangement when sung in 4-parts: last two lines —

11 Child in a stable

1 Child in a sta - ble: how love - ly is this place where God is
2 God comes in weak - ness, and to our world for love de - scends with
3 Now night is end - ed! the cha - sm that di - vides at last is

a - ble to show such per - fect grace! No prince - ly babe that
meek - ness from realms of light a - bove. This Child shall heal our
mend - ed, and God with us a - bides. For on this hap - py

smiled or pa - lace that be - guiled, in his - to - ry or
wrong, for sor - row give a song, and hope in place of
morn new glo - ry wakes the dawn; the Sun is high as -

fa - ble, could ev - er match this child with - in a sta - ble.
bleak-ness; for no-thing is so strong as God in weak - ness.
- cend - ed – to us a child is born, and night is end - ed!

Words: after E Flèchier (1632–1710), Michael Perry
Music: French traditional melody, arranged by John Barnard

Dans cette étable
5 11 6 6 6 7 11

Christ is born to be our king

12

With warmth

1 Christ is born to be our king – list - en, as the
2 Shep - herds in the fields at night hear the ti - dings,
3 Christ - ians down the a - ges tell Christ can break the

an - gels sing, to the hea - vens e - cho - ing,
see the light, find the child, in praise u - nite:
powers of hell, so that we may sing as well,

1.
'Glo - ry be to God on high!'

2.
'Glo - ry be to

3.
God on high!' 'Glo - ry be to God on high!'

Alternative tune: Ruxley (7)

Words: Michael Perry
Music: David Sanderson

Christ is born
7 7 7 7

13   Come and hear the joyful singing

1 Come and hear the joy-ful sing-ing, Al - le - lu - ia, glo - ri - a,
2 An - gels of his birth are tell - ing,
3 Choir and peo-ple, shout in won-der,

set the bells of hea - ven ring-ing: al - le - lu - ia, glo - ri - a,
prince of peace all powers ex - cell - ing;
let the mer - ry or - gan thun-der;

God the Lord has shown us fav - or – al - le - lu - ia, glo - ri - a,
death and hell can not de-feat him:
thank our God for love a-maz-ing,

Christ is born to be our sav - ior.
go to Beth-le - hem and greet him. al - le - lu - ia, glo - ri - a!
Fa - ther, Son and Spi - rit prais-ing.

Words: Michael Perry
Music: Welsh traditional melody, arranged by John Barnard

Nos Galan
8 7 8 7 D

Come and sing the Christmas story   14

1 Come and sing the Christ-mas sto - ry this ho - ly night!
2 Je - sus, sav - ior, child of Ma - ry this ho - ly night,
3 Lord of all! Let us ac - claim him this ho - ly night;

Christ is born: the hope of glo - ry dawns on our sight.
in a world con - fused and wea - ry you are our light.
king of our sal - va - tion name him, throned in the height.

Al - le - lu - ia! Earth is ring-ing with a thou-sand an-gels sing-ing –
God is in a man-ger ly - ing, man-hood tak - ing, self de - ny - ing,
Son of Man – let us a - dore him: all the earth is wait-ing for him;

hear the mes - sage they are bring-ing this ho - ly night.
life em - brac-ing, death de - fy - ing this ho - ly night.
Son of God – we bow be - fore him this ho - ly night.

Words: Michael Perry
Music: Welsh traditional melody, arranged by John Barnard

All through the night
84848884

15   I see your crib

SOPRANO

1 I see your crib – a cra - dle where the cat - tle cry,

and in the stall you lie, sweet Ma - ry's ho - ly boy. The

pro - mise, and the love, God gives – yet in the world a -

- round no place for him is found. 'No room!' they

cried – our Lord was left out - side.

SOPRANO

2 I see your face, so full of

ALTO

2 I see your face, so full of

Words: Christopher Porteous
Music: Beth Hughes, arranged by John Barnard

I see your crib
Irregular

Lift your heart

Words: Michael Perry
Music: Paul Edwards

Marston St Lawrence
7 7 7 7 and refrain

17 Mary came with meekness

1 Ma - ry came with meek - ness, Je - sus Christ to bear,
2 An - gels came with prais - es, Je - sus Christ to name,
3 Shep - herds came with tremb - ling, Je - sus Christ to see;
4 Wise men came with trea - sure, Je - sus Christ to bless –

laid the Lord of glo - ry in a man - ger there.
hea - ven's choirs ex - alt - ing him who bears our shame.
king who, at their bid - ding would their shep - herd be.
he who shares all bless - ings heaven and earth pos - sess.

We come re - joic - ing, Je - sus Christ to love:

ba - by in a man - ger – king of heaven a - bove!
ba - by in a man - ger –

ba - by in a man - ger –

Words: Paul Wigmore
Music: French traditional melody, arranged by Tom Cunningham

Noël nouvelet
65655565

O come all you children

1 O come all you child - ren to Beth - le - hem
2 O come all you child - ren, come here to the
3 O come all you child - ren, and stand by his
4 O come then you child - ren, and hark at the

town, and see here a ba - by from hea - ven come
stall and see here a child who is born Lord of
bed, and see gen - tle Ma - ry bend low at his
throng of an - gels, all crowd - ing the sky with their

down; tread soft - ly and en - ter on this sa - cred
all; more fair than the an - gels in glo - ry is
head; see Jo - seph, so hum - ble in won - der - ing
song; join in with their prais - es and joy - ful - ly

night a sta - ble with hea - ven - ly glo - ry a - light.
he, more love - ly than cher - u - bim ev - er could be.
joy, kneel down at the feet of this most ho - ly boy.
sing your loud - est thanks - giv - ing – for Je - sus the King!

Words: from the German, Paul Wigmore
Music: J A P Schultz (1747–1800), arranged by John Barnard

Ihr Kinderlein kommet
11 11 11 11

19   See him lying on a bed of straw

Unison

1 See him ly - ing on a bed of straw: a
2 Star of sil - ver, sweep a - cross the skies, show
3 An - gels, sing a - gain the song you sang, sing
4 Mine are rich - es, from your pov - er - ty, from

draf - ty sta - ble with an o - pen door; Ma -
show where Je - sus in the man - ger lies; shep -
sing the glo - ry of God's gra - cious plan; sing
from your in - no - cence, e - ter - ni - ty; mine

Ma - ry cra - dl - ing the babe she bore – the
shep - herds, swift - ly from your stu - por rise to
sing that Beth - l'em's lit - tle ba - by can
mine for - give - ness by your death for me,

prince of glo - ry is his name.
see the sav - ior of the world!
be sal - va - tion to the soul.
child of sor - row for my joy.

Words: Michael Perry
Music: Michael Perry, arranged by Stephen Coates and others

Calypso Carol
9 9 9 7 and refrain

Chorus

O now car - ry me to Beth - le - hem to

see the Lord's pure love a - gain:

just as poor as was the sta - ble then, the

prince of glo - ry when he came.

20 Sleep, Lord Jesus

1 Sleep, Lord Jesus! Mary smiling on her infant so beguiling sings a joyful lullaby.

2 Sleep, Lord Jesus! Mary grieving at the fate our sin is weaving

Words: based on the Latin, Michael Perry
Music: Tom Cunningham

Dormi Jesu
8 8 7

sings   a   so - lemn   lul - la - by.   3 Sleep,   Lord

Je - sus!   Ma - ry   dream - ing   of   this   fal - len

world's   re - deem - ing   sings   a   ho - ly   lul - la -

- by.   Sleep,   Lord   Je - sus,   lul - la - by!

21 Ring out the bells

Ring out the bells – the joy-ful news is break - ing;
ring out the bells for Je - sus Christ is born!

1 An - gels in won - der sing of his glo - ry;
2 Let all cre - a - tion wor - ship be - fore him;
3 Pro - phets have spo - ken – hark to their warn - ing:

shep - herds re - turn - ing tell us the sto - ry.
earth bring him hom - age, hea - ven a - dore him!
sha - dows are pass - ing, soon comes the morn - ing!

Words: Michael Perry
Music: English traditional melody, arranged by David Iliff

Past three a clock
4 7 4 6 10 10

When God from heaven

Words: Michael Perry
Music: English traditional melody, arranged by David Iliff

I saw three ships
8888

23 Small wonder the star

1 Small won - der the star, small won - der the light, the an - gels in cho - rus, the shep - herds in fright; but sta - ble and man - ger for God – no small won - der!

2 Small won - der the kings, small won - der they bore the gold and the in - cense, the myrrh, to a - dore; but God gives his life on a cross – no small won - der!

3 Small won - der the love, small won - der the grace, the pow - er, the glo - ry, the light of his face; but all to re - deem my poor heart – no small won - der!

Words: Paul Wigmore
Music: Paul Edwards

No small wonder
556584

Words: © 1986 by Paul Wigmore / Jubilate Hymns Ltd; USA © 1986 by Hope Publishing Company, Carol Stream IL 60188
Music: © 1986 by Paul Edwards / Jubilate Hymns Ltd; USA © 1986 by Hope Publishing Company, Carol Stream IL 60188

Lord, now let your servant

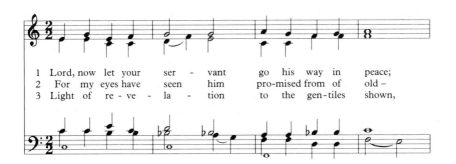

1 Lord, now let your ser - vant go his way in peace;
2 For my eyes have seen him pro-mised from of old –
3 Light of re - ve - la - tion to the gen - tiles shown,

your great love has brought me joy that will not cease:
sav - ior of all peo - ple, shep-herd of one fold:
light of Is - rael's glo - ry to the world made known.

Words: from Luke 2 (*The Song of Simeon / Nunc dimittis*), J E Seddon (1915–1983)
Music: David Wilson, arranged by John Barnard

Faithful vigil
6 5 6 5

25   Come, rejoice

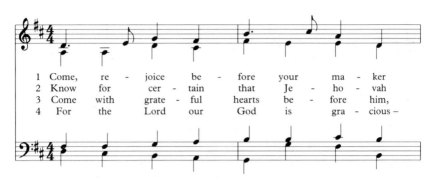

1 Come, re - joice be - fore your ma - ker
2 Know for cer - tain that Je - ho - vah
3 Come with grate - ful hearts be - fore him,
4 For the Lord our God is gra - cious –

all you peo - ples of the earth; serve the Lord your
is the true and on - ly God: we are his, for
en - ter now his courts with praise; show your thank - ful -
ev - er - last - ing in his love; and to ev - ery

God with glad - ness, come be - fore him with a song!
he has made us; we are sheep with - in his fold.
- ness to - wards him, give due hon - or to his name.
ge - ne - ra - tion his great faith - ful - ness en - dures.

Alternative tunes: Cross of Jesus (45), Gott Will's machen, Restoration (44)

Words: from Psalm 100 (*Jubilate*), Michael Baughen
Music: Noël Tredinnick

Come rejoice
8 7 8 7

Born in song

1 Born in song! God's peo-ple have al-ways been sing-ing. Born in
2 Christ is king! he left all the glo-ry of hea-ven. Christ is
3 Sing the song! God's Spi-rit is poured out a-mong us. Sing the
4 Tell the world! all pow-er to Je-sus is giv-en. Tell the
5 Then the end! Christ Je-sus shall reign in his glo-ry. Then the

song! hearts and voi-ces raised. So to-day we wor-ship to-
king! born to share in our pain; cru-ci-fied, for sin-ners a-
song! God has made us a-new; ev-ery mem-ber part of the
world! he is with us al-ways. Spread the word, that all may re-
end of all earth-ly days. Yet a-bove, the song will con-

- ge - ther: God a - lone is wor-thy to be praised.
- ton - ing; ris-en, ex - alt - ed, soon to come a - gain.
Bo - dy, giv-en his power, his will to seek and do.
- ceive him; ev - ery tongue con - fess and sing his praise.
- ti - nue; all his peo - ple still shall sing his praise!

Words: Brian Hoare
Music: Brian Hoare

Chatsworth
393799

27   Welcome to another day

1 Wel-come to an - o - ther day! Night is blind - ed:
2 Wel-come to the day of prayer with God's peo - ple;
3 Wel-come is the peace that's given, sure for ev - er;

'Wel-come', let cre - a - tion say; dark-ness end - ed.
wel - come is the joy we share at this ta - ble.
wel - come is the hope of heaven when life's o - ver.

Comes the sun-shine af - ter dew, time for la - bor;
Bread and wine from hea - ven fall: come, re - ceive it
As we work and as we pray, trust God's sto - ry:

time to love my God a - new and my neigh - bor.
that the Christ may reign in all who be - lieve it.
come then, as the dawn-ing day her - alds glo - ry!

Alternative tune: Harvey

Words: Michael Saward
Music: J D Jones (1827–1870)

Gwalchmai
7 4 7 4 D

Eternal light, shine in my heart   28

1 E - ter - nal light, shine in my heart,
2 E - ter - nal life, raise me from death,
3 Un - til by your most cost - ly grace,

e - ter - nal hope, lift up my eyes;
e - ter - nal bright - ness, help me see;
in - vit - ed by your ho - ly word,

e - ter - nal power, be my sup - port,
e - ter - nal Spi - rit, give me breath,
at last I come be - fore your face

e - ter - nal wis - dom, make me wise.
e - ter - nal Sav - ior, come to me:
to know you, my e - ter - nal God.

Alternative tunes: Ach bleib bei uns, Jacob, Seven Seas, Splendor (50)

Words: after Alcuin (c.735–804), Christopher Idle
Music: Norman Warren

Sarah Rachel
8 8 8 8 (LM)

29 Light of gladness

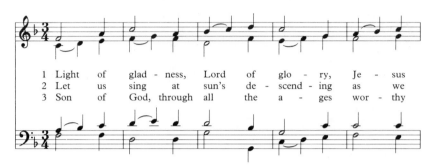

1 Light of glad - ness, Lord of glo - ry, Je - sus
2 Let us sing at sun's de - scend - ing as we
3 Son of God, through all the a - ges wor - thy

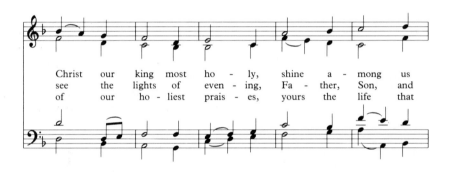

Christ our king most ho - ly, shine a - mong us
see the lights of even - ing, Fa - ther, Son, and
of our ho - liest prais - es, yours the life that

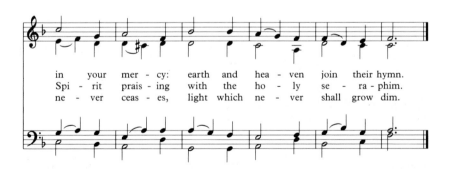

in your mer - cy: earth and hea - ven join their hymn.
Spi - rit prais - ing with the ho - ly se - ra - phim.
ne - ver ceas - es, light which ne - ver shall grow dim.

Words: from *Phos hilaron*, Christopher Idle   Quem pastores laudavere
Music: fourteenth century German melody, arranged by John Barnard   8 8 8 7

Words: © 1982 by Christopher Idle / Jubilate Hymns Ltd; USA © 1982 by Hope Publishing Company, Carol Stream IL 60188
Music arrangement: © 1988 by John Barnard / Jubilate Hymns Ltd; USA © 1988 by Hope Publishing Company, Carol Stream IL 60188

Now evening comes

Unison

1 Now even-ing comes to close the day, and soon the
2 In - to your hands, e - ter-nal Friend, we give our -
3 In wak-ing, lift our thoughts a - bove, in sleep-ing
4 To Fa - ther, Son and Spi - rit - praise, all mor - tal

si - lent hours shall ban-ish all our fears a -
-selves a - gain, and to your watch-ful care com -
guard us still, that we may rise to know your
praise be given; till sleep at last shall end our

-way, and sleep re - new our powers.
-mend all those in grief or pain.
love and prove your per - fect will.
days and we shall wake in heaven!

Alternative tunes: Creator God (40), St Bernard (39), Stracathro

Words: from *Te lucis ante terminum*
     (before the ending of the day), Michael Perry
Music: Peter White

Charnwood
8 6 8 6 (CM)

31 Bless the Lord, created things

1 Bless the Lord, cre - a - ted things, high - est
2 Sun and moon and stars of heaven, show - ery
3 Scorch - ing wind and bit - ter cold, i - cy
4 Frost - y air and fall - ing snow, clouds and
5 Springs and riv - ers, o - cean deeps, whales and
6 All on earth who serve our God, priests and

hea - vens, an - gel host; bless the Fa - ther,
wa - ters, rain and dew, stor - my gale and
bliz - zard, morn - ing mist, light and dark - ness,
light - nings, dales and hills, all that grows up -
fish - es of the sea, prowl - ing beasts and
peo - ple of the Lord, up - right, ho - ly,

Spi - rit, Son: wor - ship, all cre - a - tion.
fi - ery heat: wor - ship, all cre - a - tion.
nights and days: wor - ship, all cre - a - tion.
- on the earth: wor - ship, all cre - a - tion.
soar - ing birds: wor - ship, all cre - a - tion.
hum - ble hearts: wor - ship, all cre - a - tion.

Words: from *A Song of Creation / Benedicite*, Judy Davies
Music: Gradual, Paris (1685), arranged by David Iliff

Antiphoner
7 7 7 6

Lord of the changing year

32

1 Lord of the chang-ing year, pat-terns and col-ors bright;
2 Lord of the win-ter scene, hard-fro-zen ice and snow;
3 Lord of un-fold-ing spring, pro-mise of life to come;
4 Lord of the sum-mer days, spread-ing and green the trees;
5 Lord of the au-tumn gold, reap-ing and har-vest home,

all that we see and hear, sun-rise and star-lit night:
death where once life has been, no-thing is seen to grow;
na-ture be-gins to sing where once her tongue was dumb;
song-thrush lifts high your praise, gulls light on deep-blue seas;
sheep safe-ly in the fold, turn of the year has come:

the sea-sons, Lord in splen-dor shine,
few crea-tures roam, few birds will fly
the cro-cus blooms, the hedge-rows wake,
the warmth and wel-come of the sun
the sea-sons, Lord in splen-dor shine,

your ne-ver-fail-ing wise de-sign.
a-cross the cloud-ed Christ-mas sky:
and Eas-ter day is soon to break:
brings hap-pi-ness to ev-ery-one:
your ne-ver-fail-ing wise de-sign.

Alternative tune: Little Cornard

Words: David Mowbray
Music: David Peacock

Goldington
666688

33   The majesty of mountains

Descant

3 The glo - ry of the God - head, the Spi - rit and the

1 The ma - jes - ty of moun - tains, the sov - ereign - ty of
2 The run - ning of the ri - ver, the surg - ing of the
3 The glo - ry of the God - head, the Spi - rit and the

Son, the Fa - ther, faith - ful down the days: to them, the Three - in -

skies, the re - gal rocks that arch a - bove where veils of va - por
sea, the grass that grows, high on the hill, the flower and fruit - ing
Son, the Fa - ther, faith - ful down the days: to them, the Three - in -

- One, while life shall last be per - fect praise and high - est hon - or done!

rise, are gifts of God, the Lord of love, the wor - ship - ful, the wise.
tree, our Sav - ior sends us, by whose will all crea - tures came to be.
- One, while life shall last be per - fect praise and high - est hon - or done!

Alternative tune: Misterioso (Christopher Norton)

Words: from Psalm 104, Michael Perry
Music: John Barnard

Eythorne
768686

Jesus the Lord of love

34

1 Je - sus the Lord of love and life, draw near to
2 Give them each day your peace and joy, let no dark
3 As they have vowed to have and hold, each by the
4 Deep - en, O Lord, their love for you, and in that
5 Be to them both a guide and friend, through all the

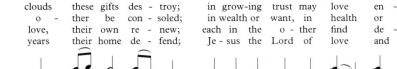

bless this man and wife; as they are now in love made
clouds these gifts des - troy; in grow-ing trust may love en -
o - ther be con - soled; in wealth or want, in health or
love, their own re - new; each in the o - ther find de -
years their home de - fend; Je - sus the Lord of love and

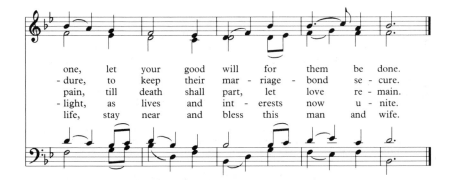

one, let your good will for them be done.
- dure, to keep their mar - riage - bond se - cure.
pain, till death shall part, let love re - main.
- light, as lives and int - erests now u - nite.
life, stay near and bless this man and wife.

Alternative tunes: Maryton, Tallis' Canon

Words: J E Seddon (1915–1983)
Music: R Harrison (1748–1810)

Warrington
8 8 8 8 (LM)

35   Lord Jesus Christ

Quietly

1 Lord Jesus Christ, in - vit - ed guest and sav - ior,
2 Give them your strength for car - ing and for serv - ing,
3 Be their de - light in joy, their hope in sor - row,

with ten - der mer - cy hear us as we pray;
give them your gra - ces – faith - ful - ness and prayer;
be their true friend in plea - sure as in pain;

grant our de - sire for those who seek your fa - vor,
make their re - solve to fol - low you un - swerv - ing,
guest of to - day and guard - ian of to - mor - row,

come with your love and bless them both to - day.
make their re - ward your peace be - yond com - pare.
turn hum - ble wa - ter in - to wine a - gain!

Alternative tune: Strength and stay

Words: Michael Perry
Music: J Barnby (1838–1896)

O perfect love
11 10 11 10

Where may that love be found   36

1 Where may that love be found up - lift-ing and com-plete, a
2 A par-ent for its child will oft-en moun-tains move; a
3 In Christ up - on the Cross Love's depths we see re - vealed; a
4 No great-er love than this dare we ex-pect to find, that
5 Give us, Lord Christ, your help to tread this nar - row way, to

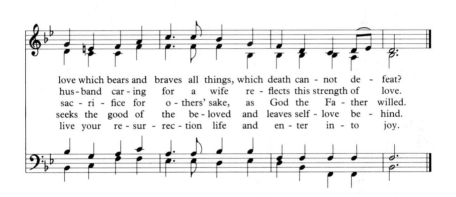

love which bears and braves all things, which death can - not de - feat?
hus-band car-ing for a wife re - flects this strength of love.
sac - ri - fice for o - thers' sake, as God the Fa - ther willed.
seeks the good of the be - loved and leaves self - love be - hind.
live your re - sur - rec - tion life and en - ter in - to joy.

Alternative tune: Carlisle

Words: David Mowbray   St George
Music: H J Gauntlett (1805–1876)   6 6 8 6 (SM)

Words: © 1989 by David Mowbray / Jubilate Hymns Ltd; USA © 1989 by Hope Publishing Company, Carol Stream IL 60188

37 When the waters cover me

1 When the wa-ters co-ver me, save me, O
God; when I look and can-not see,
when I seek what can-not be, when my
friends a-ban-don me, save me, O God.

2 You know all my guil-ty fears, thank you, O
God, you have heard with o-pen ears,
you have seen my con-trite tears, you will
bless me all the years – thank you, O God.

Words: from Psalm 69, Michael Perry
Music: David Llewellyn Green

Salvum me
747774

O Lord, my rock

1 O   Lord, my rock, to   you I   cry   when   o - thers will   not
2 I   grieve for those who   keep fine friends but   har - bor God - less
3 Yet praise the Lord – who   comes at length, who   comes to right the

hear;   to   you I   lift   my   hands on   high – [your
schemes;   who   use your works for   worth - less ends, to
wrong: to   you our shep - herd and   our strength [be

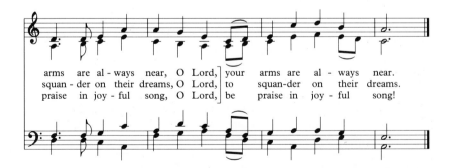

arms are al - ways near, O Lord,] your arms are al - ways near.
squan - der on their dreams, O Lord,] to squan - der on their dreams.
praise in joy - ful song, O Lord,] be praise in joy - ful song!

Alternative tunes (omitting bracketed words): Nicolaus, St Bernard (39)

Words: from Psalm 28, Michael Perry
Music: English folk song, arranged by David Iliff

Somerset
86886

39   O Lord, my rock

1 O Lord, my rock, to you I cry when
2 I grieve for those who keep fine friends but
3 Yet praise the Lord – who comes at length, who

o - thers will not hear; to you I lift my
har - bor God - less schemes; who use your works for
comes to right the wrong: to you our shep - herd

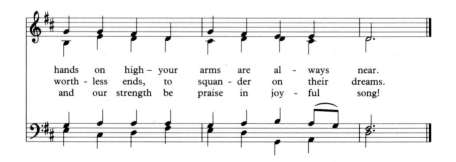

hands on high – your arms are al - ways near.
worth - less ends, to squan - der on their dreams.
and our strength be praise in joy - ful song!

Alternative tunes: Creator God (40), Nicolaus

Words: from Psalm 28, Michael Perry   St Bernard
Music: *Tochter Zion*, Cologne (1741)   8 6 8 6 (CM)

Safe in the shadow of the Lord   40

Alternative tunes: Lloyd, Stanton

Words: from Psalm 91, Timothy Dudley-Smith
Music: Norman Warren

Creator God
8 6 8 6 (CM)

41 Father God in heaven

1 Fa - ther God in heaven, Lord most high: hear your
2 May your king - dom come here on earth; may your
3 Give us dai - ly bread day by day, and for -
4 Lead us in your way, make us strong; when temp -
5 All things come from you, all are yours – king - dom,

child-ren's prayer, Lord most high: hal-lowed be your name, Lord most
will be done here on earth, as it is in heaven so on
- give our sins day by day, as we too for - give day by
- ta - tions come make us strong; save us all from sin, keep us
glo - ry, power, all are yours; take our lives and gifts, all are

high – O Lord, hear our prayer.
earth – O Lord, hear our prayer.
day – O Lord, hear our prayer.
strong – O Lord, hear our prayer.
yours – O Lord, hear our prayer.

Words: from *The Lord's Prayer*, J E Seddon (1915–1983)
Music: Traditional melody, arranged by David Peacock

Kum ba yah
8 8 8 5

How lovely is your dwelling-place   42

1 How love - ly is your dwell - ing-place, O Lord most
2 The spar - row comes to build her nest O Lord most
3 Your peo - ple come to you a - gain, O Lord most
4 In fel - low-ship your love we share, O Lord most
5 How love - ly is your dwell - ing-place O Lord most

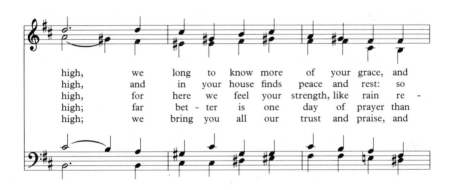

high, we long to know more of your grace, and
high, and in your house finds peace and rest: so
high, for here we feel your strength, like rain re -
high; far bet - ter is one day of prayer than
high; we bring you all our trust and praise, and

yearn to see you face to face, O Lord most high!
may we too be ev - er blessed, O Lord most high!
- fresh - ing us through toil and pain, O Lord most high!
a - ny spent in world - ly care, O Lord most high!
ask your bless - ing on our days, O Lord most high!

Words: from Psalm 84, Barbara Woollett
Music: Paul Edwards

Melchbourne
84884

43   Like a mighty river flowing

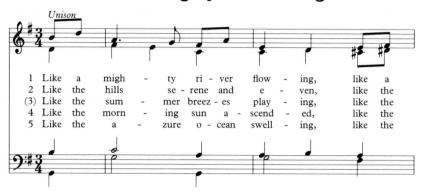

1 Like a migh - ty ri - ver flow - ing, like a
2 Like the hills se - rene and e - ven, like the
(3) Like the sum - mer breez - es play - ing, like the
4 Like the morn - ing sun a - scend - ed, like the
5 Like the a - zure o - cean swell - ing, like the

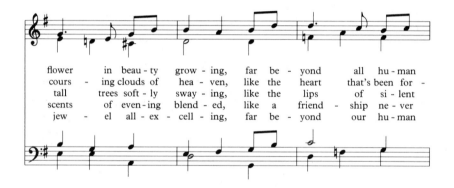

flower in beau - ty grow - ing, far be - yond all hu - man
cours - ing clouds of hea - ven, like the heart that's been for -
tall trees soft - ly sway - ing, like the lips of si - lent
scents of even - ing blend - ed, like a friend - ship ne - ver
jew - el all - ex - cell - ing, far be - yond our hu - man

know - ing is the per - fect peace of God.
- gi - ven is the per - fect peace of God.
pray - ing is the per - fect peace of God.
end - ed is the per - fect peace of God.
tell - ing is the per - fect peace of God.

Alternative tune: Quem pastores laudavere (29)

Words: Michael Perry
Music: Noël Tredinnick

Old Yeavering
8 8 8 7

Verse 3 (melody in tenor)

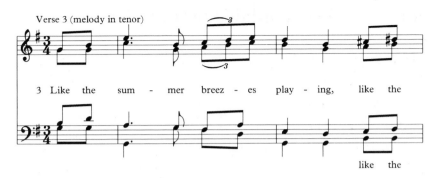

3 Like the sum - mer breez - es play - ing, like the

like the

tall trees soft - ly sway - ing, like the lips of si - lent

tall trees soft - ly sway - ing, like the lips of si - lent

pray - ing is the per - fect peace of God.

pray - ing

44
Lord all-knowing

Alternative tunes: Alton, Cross of Jesus

Words: from Psalm 139, Christopher Idle
Music: from *The Southern Harmony* 1839, arranged with descant by John Barnard

Restoration
8 7 8 7

Lord all-knowing

1 Lord all - know - ing, you have found me;
2 Lord al - migh - ty, you have made me,
3 Lord all - ho - ly, you have judged me
4 Lord all - lov - ing, you have saved me
5 Lord all - glo - rious, you re - ceive me

ev - ery sec - ret thought and word, all my ac - tions,
fash-ioned me to keep your laws; your de - sign and
by a stan - dard true and right; all the best I
in su - preme and migh - ty grace; by your Son's tri -
where your ran - somed ser - vants sing; you have spo - ken,

all my long - ings you have seen and you have heard.
your cre - a - tion— ev - ery part of me is yours.
have to of - fer with - ers in your burn - ing light.
- umph - ant mer - cy, suf - fering, dy - ing in my place.
res - cued, con-quered, Christ, our pro - phet, priest, and king!

Alternative tunes: Alton, Restoration

Words: from Psalm 139, Christopher Idle
Music: J Stainer (1840–1901)

Cross of Jesus
8 7 8 7

46   Commit your way to God

1 Com - mit your way to God the Lord – your
2 Be still be - fore the Lord and wait, and
3 Sal - va - tion comes from God a - lone – the
4 Com - mit your way to God the Lord, to

cause will shine as bright as fire; de - light to do God's
do not fret when wrong suc - ceeds; re - frain from an - ger,
faith - ful know their help is sure; to hea - ven all our
peace and truth and grace as - pire: then mer - cy shall be

ho - ly word and you shall find what you de - sire.
turn from hate, for God will pun - ish ev - il deeds.
needs are known, and in God's strength we are se - cure.
your re - ward, God's pro - mi - ses your heart's de - sire.

Alternative tunes: Wareham, Splendor (50)

Words: from Psalm 37, Michael Perry
Music: English traditional melody, arranged by David Iliff

Summercourt
8 8 8 8 (LM)

Lord of all my footsteps

Unison

1 Lord of all my foot-steps, watch-ing from a - bove,
2 O - thers moved by ma - lice spread un - truths a - round:
3 For their hope is rich - es time will yet des - troy;

keep me in the safe - ty of your per - fect love.
shall their schemes not fal - ter and their plans re - bound?
you are all my trea - sure and my last - ing joy.

Alternative tunes: Caswall, Faithful vigil (24)

Words: from Psalm 17, David Mowbray
Music: Paul Edwards

Cogenhoe
6565

Words: © 1989 by David Mowbray / Jubilate Hymns Ltd; USA © 1989 by Hope Publishing Company, Carol Stream IL 60188
Music: © 1989 by Paul Edwards / Jubilate Hymns Ltd; USA © 1989 by Hope Publishing Company, Carol Stream IL 60188

48 Lord, who may venture where you dwell

1 Lord, who may ven-ture where you dwell, or wor-ship on your ho-ly hill? The
2 They ne-ver do their neigh-bor wrong, and ut-ter no ma-li-cious word; the
3 They keep their oath at a-ny cost, and glad-ly lend, but not for gain; they

pure in heart, whose spot-less lives   by word and deed o-bey your will.
sin-ner's fol-ly they des-pise,   but hon-or those who fear the Lord.
hate all bribe-ry: come what may,   se-cure for ev-er they re-main.

Alternative tune: Breslau

Words: from Psalm 15, David Preston
Music: David Iliff

Wells House
8 8 8 8 (LM)

My soul proclaims

1 My soul pro-claims the great-ness of the Lord, and my
2 In ev-ery age, for those who fear the Lord come his
3 To Is-ra-el his ser-vant he brings help, and the

spi-rit sings for joy to my sav-ior God! His
mer-cy, and the strength of his migh-ty arm; he
pro-mise to our fa-thers is now ful-filled: for

low-ly slave he looked up-on in love: they will call me hap-py now, for
routs the proud, throws mon-archs off their thrones, while he lifts the low-ly high, fills
Christ has come ac-cord-ing to his word, and the mer-cy that he showed to

migh-ty are the works he has done, and ho-ly is his name!
hun-gry souls with food, and the rich sends emp-ty a-way.
A-bra-ham is now for his child-ren's child-ren ev-er-more.

Words: from Luke 1 (*The Song of Mary / Magnificat*), Christopher Idle
Music: Norman Warren

Andrew Mark
Irregular

50 My Lord, you wore no royal crown

1 My Lord, you wore no roy - al crown; you did not
2 You ne - ver used a kill - er's sword to end an
3 You did not live a world a - way in her - mit's
4 You made no mean or cun - ning move, chose no un -
5 You came un - e - qualled, un - de - served, to be what
6 So when I stum - ble, set me right; com - mand my

wield the powers of state, nor did you need a
un - just ty - ran - ny; your on - ly wea - pon
cell or de - sert cave, but felt our pain and
-wor - thy com - pro - mise, but carved a track of
we were meant to be; to serve in - stead of
life as you re - quire; let all your gifts be

scho - lar's gown or priest - ly robe, to make you great.
was your word, for truth a - lone could set us free.
shared each day with those you came to seek and save.
burn - ing love through tan - gles of de - ceit and lies.
be - ing served, to pay for our per - ver - si - ty.
my de - light and you, my Lord, my one de - sire.

Words: Christopher Idle
Music: M Praetorius (1571–1621), arranged by David Iliff

Splendor (Puer nobis)
8 8 8 8 (LM)

Before the heaven and earth

51

Unison

1 Be - fore the heaven and earth were
2 Though in the form of God and
3 From heights of heaven he came to
4 The Son be - came true Man and
5 O - be - dient to his death – that
6 To him en - throned on high, by

made by God's de - cree, the Son of God all -
rich be - yond com - pare, he did not stay to
this world full of sin, to meet with hun - ger,
took a ser - vant's role with low - li - ness and
death up - on a cross, no son had ev - er
an - gel hosts a - dored, all knees shall bow, and

- glo - rious dwelt in God's e - ter - ni - ty.
grasp his prize; nor did he lin - ger there.
ha - tred, hell, our life, our love to win.
self - less love he came, to make us whole.
shown such love, nor fa - ther known such loss.
tongues con - fess that Je - sus Christ is Lord.

Alternative tunes: Narenza, St George (36)

Words: from Philippians 2 (*The Song of Christ's Glory*), Brian Black and Word & Music
Music: Norman Warren

Saigon
6 6 8 6 (SM)

52 He gave his life

1 He gave his life in self-less love, for sin-ners once he came;
2 He did not come to call the good but sin-ners to re-pent;
3 They heard him call his Fa-ther's name – then 'Fin-ished!' was his cry;
4 His bo-dy bro-ken once for us is glo-rious now a-bove;

he had no stain of sin him-self but bore our guilt and shame:
it was the lame, the deaf, the blind for whom his life was spent:
like them we have for-sa-ken him and left him there to die:
the cup of bless-ing we re-ceive, a shar-ing of his love:

he took the cup of pain and death, his blood was free-ly shed;
to heal the sick, to find the lost – it was for such he came,
the sins that cru-ci-fied him then are sins his blood has cured;
as in his pres-ence we par-take, his dy-ing we pro-claim

we see his bo-dy on the cross, we share the liv-ing bread.
and round his ta-ble all may come to praise his ho-ly name.
the love that bound him to a cross our free-dom has en-sured.
un-til the hour of ma-jes-ty when Je-sus comes a-gain.

Alternative tune: Christmas Carol

Words: Christopher Porteous
Music: Andrew Maries

Selfless love
8 6 8 6 D (DCM)

I am the Bread

53

Unison

1 I am the Bread, The Bread of Life; who comes to me will ne - ver
(2) Vine, the liv - ing Vine; a - part from me you can do
(3) bread, and drink this wine, and as you do, re-ceive this

hun - ger. I am the Bread, the Bread of heaven; who feeds on
no - thing. I am the Vine, the re - al Vine: a - bide in
life of mine. All that I am I give to you, that you may

1.2.
me will ne - ver die. And as you eat, re-mem-ber
me and I in you. And as you drink, re-mem-ber
live for ev - er - - more.

3. Fine

me — my bo - dy bro - ken on the tree: my life was
me — my blood was shed up - on the tree: my life was

given to set you free, and I'm a - live for ev - er - more. 2 I am the
given to set you free, and I'm a - live for ev - er - more. 3 So eat this

Words: Brian Hoare
Music: Brian Hoare

Picket Wood
Irregular

54   O God beyond all praising

1 O God be-yond all prais - ing, we wor-ship you to -
2 *The flower of earth - ly splen - dor in time must sure - ly*
3 Then hear, O gra - cious Sav - ior, ac - cept the love we

- day and sing the love a - maz - ing that
die, its fra - gile bloom sur - ren - der to
bring, that we who know your fav - or may

songs can - not re - pay; for we can on - ly
you the Lord most high; but hid - den from all
serve you as our king; and whe - ther our to -

won - der at ev - ery gift you send, at
na - ture the e - ter - nal seed is sown — *though*
- mor - rows be filled with good or ill, we'll

Verse *2* may be omitted

Words: Michael Perry
Music: G Holst (1874–1934)

Thaxted
13 13 13 13 13 13

bless - ings with - out num - ber and mer - cies with - out
small in mor - tal sta - ture, to hea-ven's gar - den
tri - umph through our sor - rows and rise to bless you

end: we lift our hearts be - fore you and
grown: for Christ the Man from hea - ven from
still: to mar - vel at your beau - ty and

wait up - on your word, we hon - or and a -
death has set us free, and we through him are
glo - ry in your ways, and make a joy - ful

- dore you, our great and migh - ty Lord.
giv - en the fi - nal vic - to - ry!
du - ty our sac - ri - fice of praise.

55   He stood before the court

1 He stood be-fore the court on trial in-stead of us;
2 These are the crimes that tell the tale of hu-man guilt;
3 The sen-tence must be passed, the un-known pris-oner killed;
4 Shall we be judged and tried? in Christ our trial is done;

he met its power to hurt, con-demned to face the cross:
our sins, our death, our hell –on these the case is built:
the price is paid at last, the law of God ful - filled:
we live, for he has died, our con-dem - na - tion gone:

our king, ac - cused of treach - er - y; their Lord stays dumb;
to this world's powers
he takes our blame, and from that day
in Christ are we both dead and raised,

our God, a - bused for blas - phe - my!
the guilt is ours, no ans - wers come.
the ac - cu - ser's claim is wiped a - way.
a - live and free – his name be praised!

Words: Christopher Idle
Music: J B Calkin (1827–1905)

St John
666688

Words: © 1982 by Christopher Idle / Jubilate Hymns Ltd; USA © 1982 by Hope Publishing Company, Carol Stream IL 60188

The hands of Christ

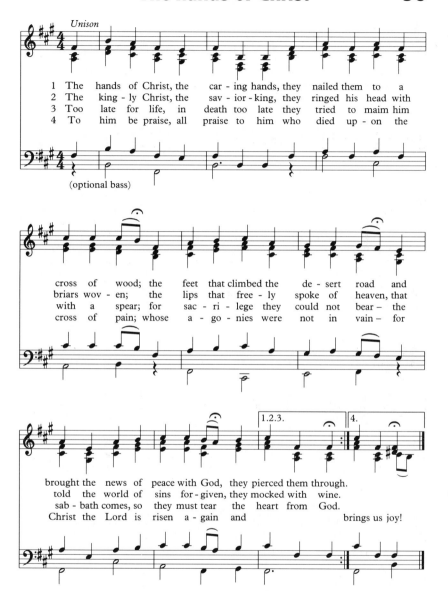

Unison

1 The hands of Christ, the car - ing hands, they nailed them to a
2 The king - ly Christ, the sav - ior - king, they ringed his head with
3 Too late for life, in death too late they tried to maim him
4 To him be praise, all praise to him who died up - on the

(optional bass)

cross of wood; the feet that climbed the de - sert road and
briars wov - en; the lips that free - ly spoke of heaven, that
with a spear; for sac - ri - lege they could not bear – the
cross of pain; whose a - go - nies were not in vain – for

[1.2.3.] [4.]

brought the news of peace with God, they pierced them through.
told the world of sins for - given, they mocked with wine.
sab - bath comes, so they must tear the heart from God.
Christ the Lord is risen a - gain and brings us joy!

This melody is particularly effective when sung unaccompanied.
Pianists are recommended to make sparing use of the optional bass,
perhaps only for verses 2 and 4.

Words: Michael Perry
Music: Simon Beckley, arranged by John Barnard

Medfield Street
88884

57   A purple robe

1 A pur - ple robe, a crown of thorn, a reed in his right
4 He hangs, by whom the world was made, be - neath the dark - ened

hand;   be - fore the sol - diers' spite and scorn I
sky;   the ev - er - last - ing ran - som paid, I

see my sav - ior stand.   2 He bears be - tween the
see my sav - ior die.   5 He shares on high his

Ro - man guard the weight of all our woe;   a
Fa - ther's throne who once in mer - cy came;   for

Words: Timothy Dudley-Smith
Music: David Wilson, arranged by Noël Tredinnick

A purple robe
8 6 8 6 Triple

58 Lord of the cross of shame

1 Lord of the cross of shame, set my cold heart a - flame
2 Lord of the emp - ty tomb, born of a vir - gin's womb,
3 Lord of my life to - day, teach me to live and pray

with love for you, my sav - ior and my mas - ter;
tri - umph - ant o - ver death, its power de - feat - ed;
as one who knows the joy of sins for - giv - en;

who on that lone - ly day bore all my sins a - way,
how glad - ly now I sing your praise, my ris - en king,
so may I ev - er be, now and e - ter - nal - ly,

and saved me from the judg - ment and dis - as - ter.
and wor - ship you, in hea - ven's splen - dor seat - ed.
one with my fel - low - ci - ti - zens in hea - ven.

Words: Michael Saward
Music: Michael Baughen, arranged by Noël Tredinnick

Cross of shame
6 6 11 D

Comes Mary to the grave

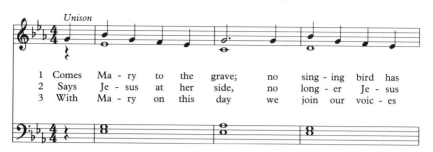

1 Comes Ma - ry to the grave; no sing - ing bird has
2 Says Je - sus at her side, no long - er Je - sus
3 With Ma - ry on this day we join our voic - es

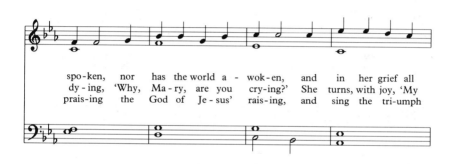

spo-ken, nor has the world a - wok-en, and in her grief all
dy - ing, 'Why, Ma - ry, are you cry-ing?' She turns, with joy, 'My
prais-ing the God of Je - sus' rais-ing, and sing the tri-umph

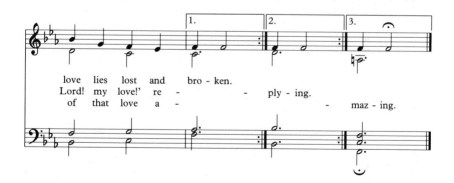

love lies lost and bro - ken.
Lord! my love!' re - ply - ing.
of that love a - maz - ing.

Alternative tunes: Church Close, Paschal Dawn

Words: from John 20, Michael Perry
Music: Norman Warren

Easter Morning
6 7 7 11

60 Exult, creation round God's throne

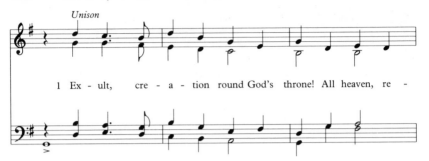

1 Ex - ult, cre - a - tion round God's throne! All heaven, re -

- joice! All an - gels, sing! Sal - va - tion's trum - pet

sound a - loud for Je - sus Christ, our ris - en king.

Words: from *Exsultet* (Easter song of praise), Christopher Idle
Music: Paul Edwards

Fenny Stratford
6 7 7 11

Harmony

2 Ex - ult, O earth, in ra - diant hope; in Christ's ma -
3 Ex - ult, all Christ-ians, one in praise with our Je -

- jes - tic splen - dor shine! The Lord is here, the
- ru - sa - lem a - bove! This roof shall ring with

vic - tory won, the dark-ness drowned in light di - vine.
Eas - ter songs that ec - ho Christ's re - deem - ing love.

Optional verse

Exult in God, pure well of truth;
in Christ, fresh fountainhead of grace;
in Spirit, flowing stream of life –
eternal Joy our hearts embrace.

This version is compatible with the unison setting.
Original key: A major.
If the piece is sung by choir alone the original key is preferable.

61   I love you, O Lord

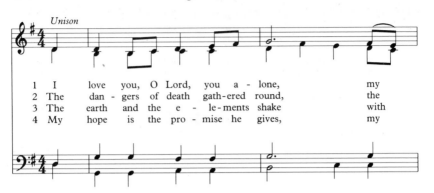

Unison

```
1 I      love   you, O Lord,   you a - lone,         my
2 The    dan - gers of death   gath-ered round,      the
3 The    earth  and the  e  -  le-ments shake         with
4 My     hope   is  the  pro - mise he  gives,        my
```

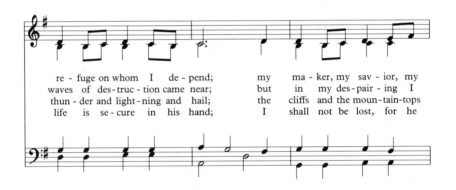

```
re - fuge on whom  I  de - pend;     my   ma - ker, my sav - ior, my
waves of des-truc-tion came near;    but  in   my des-pair - ing  I
thun - der and light-ning and  hail; the  cliffs and the moun-tain-tops
life  is se - cure in  his hand;     I    shall not be lost, for he
```

```
own,     my    hope and my trust with-out   end.    The
found    the   Lord who re-leased me from    fear.    I
break    and   mor - tals are fee - ble and  pale.   His
lives!   He    comes to my aid –  I shall    stand!  Lord
```

Alternative tune: Trewen

Words: from Psalm 18, Christopher Idle   Jane
Music: David Peacock   8 8 8 8 D

Lord is my strength and my song, de -
called for his help in my pain, to
jus - tice is full and com - plete, his
God, you are power - ful to save, your

- fen - der and guide of my ways; my mas - ter to whom I be -
God my sal - va - tion I cried; he brought me his com - fort a -
mer - cy to us has no end; the clouds are a path for his
Spi - rit will spur me to pray; your Son has de - feat - ed the

- long, my God who shall have all my praise.
- gain, I live by the strength he sup - plied.
feet, he comes on the wings of the wind.
grave: I trust and I praise you to - day!

62   Now lives the Lamb of God

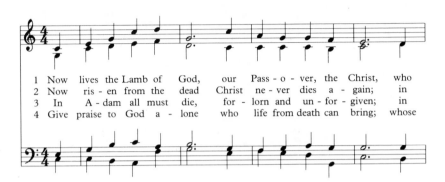

1 Now lives the Lamb of God, our Pass - o - ver, the Christ, who
2 Now ris - en from the dead Christ ne - ver dies a - gain; in
3 In A - dam all must die, for - lorn and un - for - given; in
4 Give praise to God a - lone who life from death can bring; whose

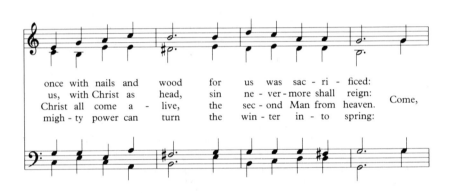

once with nails and wood for us was sac - ri - ficed:
us, with Christ as head, sin ne - ver - more shall reign:
Christ all come a - live, the sec - ond Man from heaven. Come,
migh - ty power can turn the win - ter in - to spring:

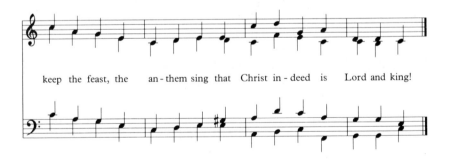

keep the feast, the an - them sing that Christ in - deed is Lord and king!

Alternative tune: Gopsal (73)

Words: from *The Easter Anthems*, David Mowbray
Music: C Steggall (1826–1905)

Christchurch
666688

Name of all majesty

63

1 Name of all ma - jes - ty, fa - thom - less mys - te - ry,
2 Child of our des - ti - ny, God from e - ter - ni - ty,
3 Sav - ior of Cal - va - ry, cost - li - est vic - to - ry,
4 Source of all sove - reign - ty, light, im - mor - ta - li - ty,

king of the a - ges by an - gels a - dored;
love of the Fa - ther on sin - ners out - poured;
dark - ness de - feat - ed and Ed - en re - stored;
life ev - er - last - ing and hea - ven as - sured;

power and au - tho - ri - ty, splen - dor and dig - ni - ty,
see now what God has done send - ing his on - ly Son,
born as a man to die, nailed to a cross on high,
so with the ran - somed, we praise him e - ter - nal - ly,

bow to his mas - te - ry – Je - sus is Lord!
Christ the be - lov - ed One – Je - sus is Lord!
cold in the grave to lie – Je - sus is Lord!
Christ in his ma - jes - ty – Je - sus is Lord!

Words: Timothy Dudley-Smith
Music: Michael Baughen, arranged by Noël Tredinnick

Majestas
66556664

64 Christ triumphant, ever reigning

Alternative tune: Christ triumphant

Words: Michael Saward
Music: John Barnard

Guiting Power
858579

65 Sing a new song of God

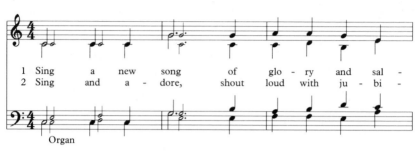

1 Sing a new song of glo - ry and sal -
2 Sing and a - dore, shout loud with ju - bi -

- va - tion, through all the earth let
- la - tion, tell of the truth and

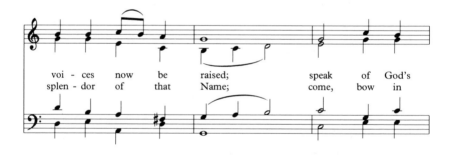

voi - ces now be raised; speak of God's
splen - dor of that Name; come, bow in

migh - ty power in eve - ry na - tion —
wor - ship, all of God's cre - a - tion —

Alternative tune: Strength and stay

Words: from Psalm 96, Stephen Horsfall
Music: Michael Baughen, arranged by David Iliff and John Barnard

Lord of the years
11 10 11 10

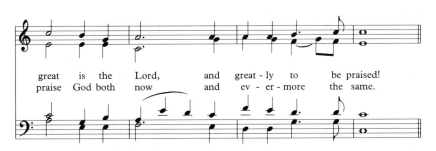

great   is   the   Lord,   and   great - ly   to   be praised!
praise God both now   and   ev - er - more   the same.

Descant

3 Say: God's   rule   is   ne - ver -

3 Say   to   the   earth: God's   rule   is   ne - ver -

- end   -   ing,   soon Christ shall   come   to

- end   -   ing,   soon   Christ shall   come   to

He lives in us

1 He lives in us, the Christ of God, his Spi - rit joins with ours;
2 Our pangs of guilt and fears of death are Sa - tan's stra - ta - gems –
3 God gave the Son to save us all – no great-er love is known!

he brings to us the Fa - ther's grace with powers be - yond our powers.
by Je - sus Christ who died for us God par - dons: who con - demns?
And shall that love a - ban - don us who have be - come Christ's own?

And if en - tic - ing sin grows strong, when hu - man na - ture fails,
And when we can - not feel our faith, nor bring our-selves to pray,
For God has raised him from the grave, in this we stand as - sured;

God's Spi - rit in our in - ner self fights with us, and pre - vails.
the Spi - rit pleads with God for us in words we could not say.
so none can tear us from the love of Je - sus Christ our Lord.

Alternative tune: Kingsfold

Words: from Romans 8, Michael Perry
Music: Chris Bowater, arranged by Noël Tredinnick

Rachel
8 6 8 6 (DCM)

67 Spirit of holiness

Spi - rit of ho - li - ness, wis - dom and faith - ful - ness,

wind of the Lord, blow - ing strong - ly and free:

strength of our serv - ing and joy of our wor - ship-ping –

Fine

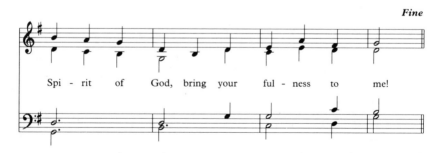

Spi - rit of God, bring your ful - ness to me!

Words: Christopher Idle
Music: Traditional melody, arranged by John Barnard

Blow the wind southerly
12 10 12 10 13 10 13 10

1 You came to in - ter - pret and teach us ef - fec - tive - ly
2 You came with your gifts to sup - ply all our pov - er - ty,

all that the Sav - ior has spo - ken and done; to
pour - ing your love on the church in her need; you

glo - ri - fy Je - sus is all your ac - ti - vi - ty –
came with your fruit for our growth to ma - tu - ri - ty,

D.C.

Pro - mise and Gift of the Fa - ther and Son:
rich - ly re - fresh - ing the souls that you feed:

68   May we, O Holy Spirit

Unison

1 May we, O Ho-ly Spi-rit, bear your fruit –
2 May pa-tience stem the harm-ful word and deed,
3 May faith-ful-ness en-dure, yet as we grow

your joy and
and kind-ness
may gen-tle-

peace per-vade each word we say; may love be-come of life the
seek the good a-mong the wrong; may good-ness far be-yond our
-ness lend cour-age to the weak; and in our self-re-straint help

ve-ry root, and grow more deep and strong with ev-ery day.
lips pro-ceed, as ma-ni-fest in ac-tion as in song.
us to know the grace that made the King of Hea-ven meek.

Alternative tunes: Beacon Hill (5), Sursum corda

Words: Paul Wigmore
Music: Paul Edwards

Lavendon
10 10 10 10

Clothed in kingly majesty

69

1 Clothed in king-ly ma-jes-ty, robed in re-gal power, God is o-ver all.

2 Lord of all, un-shake-a-ble, throned be-yond all time,

3 Great-er than the ri-ver's roar and the surg-ing sea, God is o-ver all.

4 Change-less as his law's de-crees, crowned our ho-ly king,

The Harmony and Unison versions are not harmonically compatible.

Words: from Psalm 93, Michael Saward
Music: Norman Warren, harmony by John Barnard

Kingly majesty
7 5 5

70   Great and wonderful your deeds

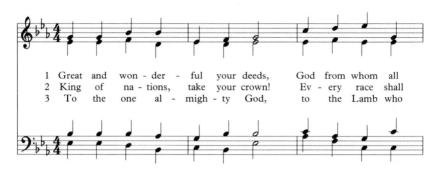

1 Great and won - der - ful your deeds, God from whom all
2 King of na - tions, take your crown! Ev - ery race shall
3 To the one al - migh - ty God, to the Lamb who

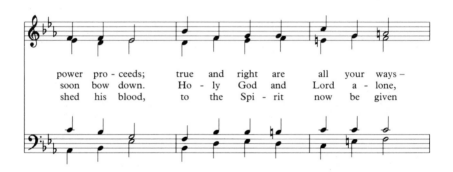

power pro - ceeds; true and right are all your ways –
soon bow down. Ho - ly God and Lord a - lone,
shed his blood, to the Spi - rit now be given

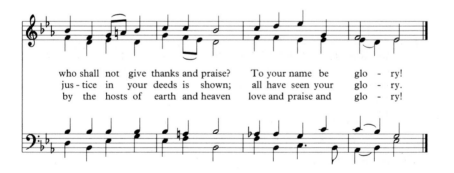

who shall not give thanks and praise? To your name be glo - ry!
jus - tice in your deeds is shown; all have seen your glo - ry.
by the hosts of earth and heaven love and praise and glo - ry!

Words: from *Great and Wonderful*, Christopher Idle   Württemberg
Music: *Hundert Arien* Dresden (1694)   77776

My Lord of light

1 My Lord of light who made the worlds, in wis-dom you have spo-ken; but those who heard your wise com-mands your ho-ly law have bro-ken.

2 My Lord of love who knew no sin, a sin-ner's death en - dur-ing: for us you wore a crown of thorns, a crown of life se - cur-ing.

3 My Lord of life who came in fire when Christ was high a - scend-ed: your burn-ing love is now re - leased, our days of fear are end-ed.

4 My Lord of lords, one Tri - ni - ty, to your pure name be gi - ven all glo-ry now and ev - er-more, all praise in earth and hea - ven.

Words: Christopher Idle
Music: English traditional melody, arranged by Noël Tredinnick

Barbara Allen
8 7 8 7

72   O Trinity, O Trinity

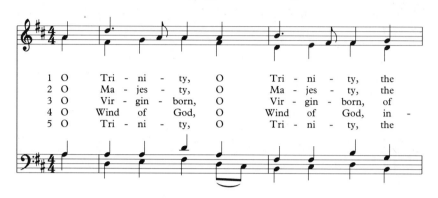

1 O   Tri - ni - ty,   O   Tri - ni - ty,   the
2 O   Ma - jes - ty,   O   Ma - jes - ty,   the
3 O   Vir - gin - born,   O   Vir - gin - born,   of
4 O   Wind of   God,   O   Wind of   God,   in -
5 O   Tri - ni - ty,   O   Tri - ni - ty,   the

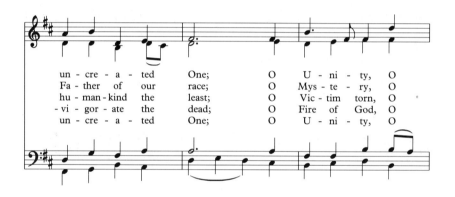

un - cre - a - ted   One;   O   U - ni - ty,   O
Fa - ther of   our   race;   O   Mys - te - ry,   O
hu - man - kind the   least;   O   Vic - tim torn,   O
- vi - gor - ate the   dead;   O   Fire of   God,   O
un - cre - a - ted   One;   O   U - ni - ty,   O

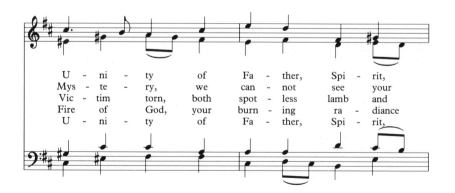

U - ni - ty   of   Fa - ther,   Spi - rit,
Mys - te - ry,   we   can - not   see   your
Vic - tim torn,   both   spot - less   lamb   and
Fire of   God,   your   burn - ing   ra - diance
U - ni - ty   of   Fa - ther,   Spi - rit,

Words: from the Lenten Triodion of the Orthodox Church, Michael Saward
Music: Kenneth W Coates

Trinity
86867788

Son: you   are with - out be - gin - ning,   your
face: your   jus - tice   is   un - swerv - ing,   your
priest: you   died and   rose vic - tor - ious,   you
spread: your   fruit our   lives re - new - ing,   your
Son: you   are with - out be - gin - ning,   your

life   is   ne - ver - end - ing;
love   is   o - ver - power - ing;
reign a - bove all - glo - rious;   and   though our tongues are
gifts, the church trans - form - ing;
life   is   ne - ver - end - ing;

earth - bound clay,   light them with flam - ing   fire to - day.

73   Take heart and praise our God

1 Take heart and praise our God – re - joice and clap your
2 Take heart, but sing with fear, ex - alt God's wor - thy
3 Take heart for fu - ture days, for tasks as yet un -
4 Take heart and trust in God the Fa - ther and the

hands – whose power our foe sub - dued, whose
Name – with mind a - lert and clear Love's
- known – the God whose name we praise is
Son – God is our strength and shield, the

mer - cy ev - er stands:
pro - vi - dence a - claim:
seat - ed on the throne: let trum - pets sound and
Spi - rit guides us on:

peo - ple sing, the Lord through all the earth is king!

Alternative tune: Christchurch (62)

Words: from Psalm 47, David Mowbray
Music: melody and bass G F Handel (1685–1759)

Gopsal
666688

Words: © 1986 by David Mowbray / Jubilate Hymns Ltd; USA © 1986 by Hope Publishing Company, Carol Stream IL 60188

This is the truth which we proclaim 74

1 This is the truth which we pro - claim,
2 This is the grave in which we lie:
3 This is the sac - ra - ment of birth:
4 This is the co - ve - nant of grace –
5 This is the badge we proud - ly wear:

God makes a pro - mise firm and sure; marked by this sign made
pierced to the heart by sin's sharp sword, ris - en with Christ, to
sealed by a Sav - ior's death for sin, trust in his mer - cy,
God to the na - tions of - fers love; peo - ple of ev - ery
washed by our God, the Three - in - One; wel-comed in fel - low -

in that name, here, for our sick - ness, God's own cure.
self we die, and live to praise our reign - ing Lord.
all on earth, o - pen your hearts and let him in!
tribe and race, born by the Spi - rit from a - bove.
- ship, we share hope of e - ter - nal life be - gun.

Alternative tune: Fulda

Words: Michael Saward
Music: J Hatton (died 1793)

Duke Street
8 8 8 8 (LM)

75 Jesus, Savior of the world

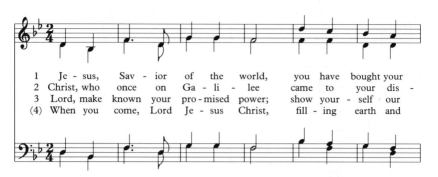

1 Je - sus, Sav - ior of the world, you have bought your
2 Christ, who once on Ga - li - lee came to your dis -
3 Lord, make known your pro - mised power; show your - self our
(4) When you come, Lord Je - sus Christ, fill - ing earth and

peo - ple's free - dom by your cross, your life laid down:
- ci - ples' res - cue: we, like them, cry out for help –
strong de - liv - erer: so our prayer shall turn to praise –
heaven with won - der, come to make us one with you –

now bring in your glo-rious king - dom. Come to help us!
free us from our sins, we ask you. Come to save us!
hear us, stay with us for ev - er. Come to rule us!
heirs of life, to reign in splen - dor. Al - le - lu - ia!

Words: from *Saviour of the World*, Christopher Idle
Music: H J Gauntlett (1805–1876), descant and arrangement by John Barnard

St Albinus
78784

Descant

4 When you come, Lord Je - sus Christ, fill - ing earth and

Unison

4 When you come, Lord Je - sus Christ, fill - ing earth and

heaven with won - der, come to make us one with you –

heaven with won - der, come to make us one with you –

heirs of life, to reign in splen - dor. Al - le - lu - ia!

heirs of life, to reign in splen - dor. Al - le - lu - ia!

76 How good a thing it is

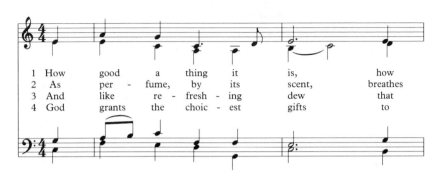

1 How good a thing it is, how
2 As per - fume, by its scent, breathes
3 And like re - fresh - ing dew that
4 God grants the choic - est gifts to

plea - sant to be - hold, when all God's peo - ple
fra - grance all a - round, so life it - self will
falls up - on the hills, true un - ion sheds its
those who live in peace; to them such bless - ings

live at one, the law of love up - hold!
sweet - er be where u - ni - ty is found.
gen - tle grace, and deep - er love in - stills.
shall a - bound and ev - er - more in - crease.

Alternative tunes: Franconia (91), St George (36), Venice (77)

Words: from Psalm 133, J E Seddon (1915–1983)
Music: John Barnard

Steeple Ashton
6 6 8 6 (SM)

How good a thing it is 77

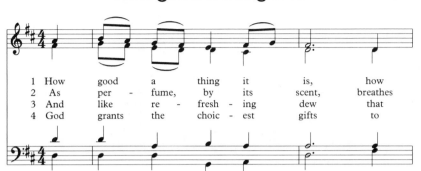

1 How good a thing it is, how
2 As per - fume, by its scent, breathes
3 And like re - fresh - ing dew that
4 God grants the choic - est gifts to

plea - sant to be - hold, when all God's peo - ple
fra - grance all a - round, so life it - self will
falls up - on the hills, true u - nion sheds its
those who live in peace; to them such bless - ings

live at one, the law of love up - hold!
sweet - er be where u - ni - ty is found.
gen - tle grace, and deep - er love in - stills.
shall a - bound and ev - er - more in - crease.

Alternative tunes: Franconia (91), St George (36)

Words: from Psalm 133, J E Seddon (1915–1983)   Venice
Music: W Amps (1824–1918)   6 6 8 6 (SM)

78   Church of God, elect and glorious

1 Church of God, e - lect and glo-rious, ho - ly na-tion, cho - sen race;
2 God has called you out of dark-ness in - to this most mar-velous light;
3 Once you were an a - lien peo-ple, strang-ers to God's heart of love;
4 Church of God, e - lect and ho - ly, be the peo-ple Christ in - tends;

called as God's own spe-cial peo-ple, roy - al priests and heirs of grace:
bring-ing truth to life with-in you, turn-ing blind-ness in - to sight:
Christ has brought you home in mer-cy, ci - ti - zens of heaven a - bove:
strong in faith and swift to ans-wer each com-mand your mas-ter sends:

know the pur - pose of your call-ing, show to all God's migh-ty deeds;
let your light so shine a - round you that God's name is glo - ri - fied;
let his love flow out to o - thers, let them feel the Sav-ior's care;
roy - al priests, ful - fill your call - ing through your sac - ri - fice and prayer;

tell of love which knows no lim - its, grace which meets all hu - man needs.
and all find fresh hope and pur-pose in Christ Je - sus cru - ci - fied.
that they too may know his wel-come and his count-less bless-ings share.
give your lives in joy - ful ser-vice – sing his praise, his love de - clare.

Words: from 1 Peter 2, J E Seddon (1915–1983)
Music: A Sullivan (1842–1900)

Lux Eoi
8 7 8 7 D

Go forth and tell

79

Unison

1 Go forth and tell! O church of God, a-wake! God's
2 Go forth and tell! God's love em-bra-ces all, and
3 Go forth and tell! where still the dark-ness lies; in
4 Go forth and tell! The doors are op-en wide: share
5 Go forth and tell! O church of God, a-rise! go

sav-ing news to all the na-tions take;
will in grace re-spond to all who call:
wealth or want, the sin-ner sure-ly dies:
God's good gifts – let no one be de-nied;
in the strength which Christ your Lord sup-plies;

pro-claim Christ Je-sus, sav-ior, Lord, and king,
how shall they call if they have ne-ver heard
give us, O Lord, con-cern of heart and mind,
live out your life as Christ your Lord shall choose,
go till all na-tions his great name a-dore

that all the world his wor-thy praise may sing.
the gra-cious in-vi-ta-tion of the Word?
a love like yours which cares for hu-man-kind.
your ran-somed powers for his sole glo-ry use.
and serve him, Lord and king for ev-er-more.

Alternative tunes: Go forth, Woodlands

Words: J E Seddon (1915–1983)
Music: John Barnard

Yanworth
10 10 10 10

80   We give God thanks

Unison

1 We give God thanks for those who knew the touch of
(2) prayer for all who go re - ly - ing
(3) - cate our skills and time to those who
(4) touch of heal - ing grace lives on with -

Je - sus' heal - ing love; they trust - ed him to make them
on God's grace and power, to help the an - xious and the
suf - fer where we live, to bring such com - fort as we
- in our will - ing care; by thought and prayer and gifts we

whole, to give them peace, their guilt
ill, to heal their wounds, their lives
can to meet their need, their pain
prove his mer - cy still, his love

1.2.3.   **4.**

re - move.   2 We of - fer
re - store.   3 We de - di -
re - lieve.   4 So Je - sus'
we share.

Words: Michael Perry
Music: Colin Avery

Newinnton
8 8 8 8 (LM)

We give God thanks

1 We give God thanks for those who knew the
2 We of - fer prayer for all who go re -
3 We de - di - cate our skills and time to
4 So Je - sus' touch of heal - ing grace lives

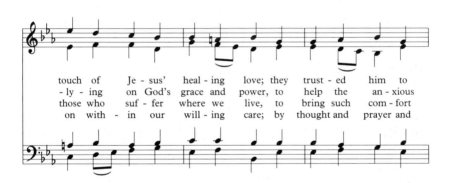

touch of Je - sus' heal - ing love; they trust - ed him to
- ly - ing on God's grace and power, to help the an - xious
those who suf - fer where we live, to bring such com - fort
on with - in our will - ing care; by thought and prayer and

make them whole, to give them peace, their guilt re - move.
and the ill, to heal their wounds, their lives re - store.
as we can to meet their need, their pain re - lieve.
gifts we prove his mer - cy still, his love we share.

Words: Michael Perry
Music: S Webbe the elder (1740–1816)

Melcombe
8 8 8 8 (LM)

Words: © 1982 by Michael Perry / Jubilate Hymns Ltd; USA © 1982 by Hope Publishing Company, Carol Stream IL 60188

82   With loving hands

1 With lov - ing hands, at work a - mong the
2 With wound - ed hands, out - stretched up - on a
3 With plead - ing hands, to - wards the world he

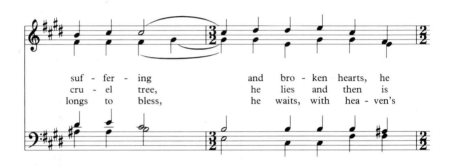

suf - fer - ing and bro - ken hearts, he
cru - el tree, he lies and then is
longs to bless, he waits, with hea - ven's

min - is - ters, who is their king.
lift - ed up in a - go - ny.
life to fill our emp - ti - ness.

Words: Randle Manwaring
Music: Noël Tredinnick

Enigma
4 8 8 4

Words: © 1982 by Randle Manwaring; USA © 1982 by Hope Publishing Company, Carol Stream IL 60188
Music: © 1982 by Noël Tredinnick / Jubilate Hymns Ltd; USA © 1982 by Hope Publishing Company, Carol Stream IL 60188

God of light and life's creation 83

Alternative tune: All Saints

Words: from 1 Kings 8, Michael Perry
Music: David Iliff

Bushey Hall
878777

84   God is our fortress and our rock

1 God is our fort - ress and our rock, our migh - ty help in
2 Our hope is fixed on Christ a - lone – the Man, of God's own
3 The word of God will not be slow while de - mon hordes sur -

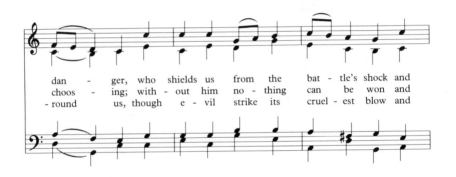

dan - ger, who shields us from the bat - tle's shock and
choos - ing; with - out him no - thing can be won and
- round us, though e - vil strike its cruel - est blow and

thwarts the de - vil's an - ger: for still the prince of
fight - ing must be los - ing: so let the powers ac -
death and hell con - found us: for e - ven if dis -

Words: from Psalm 46, after Martin Luther, Michael Perry
Music: Martin Luther (1483–1546)

Ein' feste Burg
Version A – 8 7 8 7 6 6 6 6 7

night   pro - longs   his   e - vil   fight;   he
- cursed   come   on   and   do   their   worst –   the
- tress   should   take   all   we   pos - sess,   and

us - es   ev - ery   skill   to   work   his   wick - ed
Son   of   God   shall   ride   to   bat - tle   at   our
those   who   mean   us   ill   should   rav - age,   wreck,   or

will –   no   earth - ly   force   is   like   him.
side,   and   he   shall   have   the   vic - tory.
kill,   God's   king - dom   is   im - mor - tal!

85 God is our fortress and our rock

('rhythmic')

1 God is our fort - ress and our rock, our migh - ty
2 Our hope is fixed on Christ a - lone – the Man, of
3 The word of God will not be slow while de - mon

help in dan - ger, who shields us from the
God's own choos - ing; with - out him no - thing
hordes sur - round us, though e - vil strike its

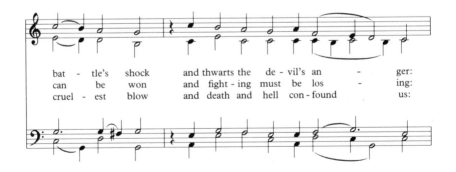

bat - tle's shock and thwarts the de - vil's an - ger:
can be won and fight - ing must be los - ing:
cruel - est blow and death and hell con - found us:

Words: from Psalm 46, after Martin Luther, Michael Perry
Music: Martin Luther (1483–1546)

Ein' feste Burg ('rhythmic')
878765567

for still   the prince of night   pro - longs   e - vil's fight;
so   let   the powers ac-cursed   come   try   do   their worst –
for though   we   meet dis-tress,   lose   all   we   pos - sess;

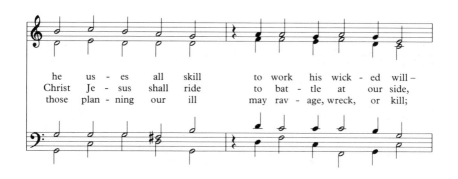

he   us - es   all   skill   to work   his wick - ed will –
Christ Je - sus shall ride   to bat - tle   at   our side,
those plan - ning our   ill   may rav - age, wreck, or kill;

no   earth - ly   force   is   like   him.
and   he   shall have   the vic   -   tory.
God's king - dom   is   im - mor   -   tal!

86   We have heard, O Lord our God

1 We have heard,   O Lord our God   the sto - ry of your
2 You are great,   O Lord our God,   we trust - ed in your
3 Yet to - day,   O Lord our God,   the weak – who once were

grace;   and how you gave to us this land,   de - fend - ing
name;   we did not tri-umph by the sword,   but through the
strong –   cry out to you, 'O come, a - rise,   re - veal your

us with your right hand   and show - ing us your face.
vic-tory of your word   you put our foes to shame.
light to dark-ened eyes,   and turn our sighs to song!'

Words: from Psalm 44, Michael Perry
Music: Peter White

Great Glen
75886

God of gods, we sound his praises 87

1 God of gods, we sound his prais - es, high - est heaven its ho - mage brings;
2 Christ-ians in their hearts en-throne him, tell his prais - es wide a - broad;
3 Hail the Christ, the King of glo - ry, he whose praise the an - gels cry;
4 Lord, we look for your re - turn - ing; teach us so to walk your ways,

earth and all cre - a - tion rais - es glo - ry to the King of kings:
pro-phets, priests, a - pos-tles own him mar-tyrs' crown and saints' re - ward.
born to share our hu-man sto - ry, love and la - bor, grieve and die:
hearts and minds your will di-scern-ing, lives a - light with joy and praise.

ho - ly, ho - ly, ho - ly, name him, Lord of all his hosts pro-claim him;
Three-in - One his glo - ry shar-ing, earth and heaven his praise de - clar-ing,
by his cross his work com-plet - ed, sin-ners ran-somed, death de - feat-ed;
In your love and care en-fold us, by your con - stan - cy up-hold us;

to the ev - er - last-ing Fa - ther ev - ery tongue in tri - umph sings.
praise the high ma - jes - tic Fa - ther, praise the ev - er - last - ing Lord!
in the glo - ry of the Fa-ther Christ a - scend-ed reigns on high.
may your mer-cy, Lord and Fa-ther, keep us now and all our days!

Words: from *Te Deum*, Timothy Dudley-Smith
Music: Christian Strover

God of gods
87878887

Words: © 1970 by Timothy Dudley-Smith; USA © 1973 by Hope Publishing Company, Carol Stream IL 60188
Music: © 1973 by Christian Strover / Jubilate Hymns Ltd; USA © 1973 by Hope Publishing Company, Carol Stream IL 60188

88   Bring to the Lord a glad new song

Bring to the Lord a glad new song, child-ren of grace ex-tol your king: your love and praise to God be-long – to in-stru-ments of mu - sic,

Words: from Psalms 149 and 150, Michael Perry
Music: C H H Parry (1848–1918)

Jerusalem
8 8 8 8 D (DLM)

given! With strings and brass and wind re-joice – then, join our praise in full ac -

allargando *ff*   **rit.**

- cord   all liv-ing things   with breath and voice;   let ev-ery

crea-ture praise the   Lord!

8va

89 Here from all nations

1 Here from all nations, all tongues, and all peo - ples,
2 These have come out of the hard - est op - pres - sion,
3 Gone is their thirst and no more shall they hun - ger,
4 He will go with them to clear liv - ing wa - ter
5 Bless - ing and glo - ry and wis - dom and pow - er

count - less the crowd but their voi - ces are one;
now they may stand in the pre - sence of God,
God is their shel - ter, his power at their side;
flow - ing from springs which his mer - cy sup - plies;
be to the Sav - ior a - gain and a - gain;

vast is the sight and ma - jes - tic their sing - ing –
serv - ing their Lord day and night in his tem - ple,
sun shall not pain them, no burn - ing will tor - ture,
gone is their grief and their tri - als are o - ver –
might and thanks - giv - ing and hon - or for ev - er

'God has the vic - tory: he reigns from the throne!'
ran - somed and cleansed by the Lamb's pre - cious blood.
Je - sus the Lamb is their shep - herd and guide.
God wipes a - way ev - ery tear from their eyes.
be to our God: Al - le - lu - ia! A - men.

Alternative tune: Epiphany Hymn

Words: from Revelation 7, Christopher Idle
Music: *Paris Antiphoner* (1681)

O quanta qualia
11 10 11 10

Glory and honor

1 Glo - ry and hon - or, wis - dom and splen - dor,
2 Once was the ran - som paid for our free - dom –

Lord of cre - a - tion, are yours a - lone:
from ev - ery na - tion with you we reign:

all of earth's crea - tures in ex - ul - ta - tion
yours be the prais - es, high ve - ne - ra - tion,

sing to the Lamb up - on the throne.
wor - ship for ev - er - more. A - men.

Words: from Revelation 4, 5, *Glory and honor*, Michael Perry
Music: *Silesian Folk Songs* Leipzig (1842)

Schönster Herr Jesu
559558

Words: © 1989 by Michael Perry / Jubilate Hymns Ltd; USA © 1989 by Hope Publishing Company, Carol Stream IL 60188

91 The earth is yours, O God

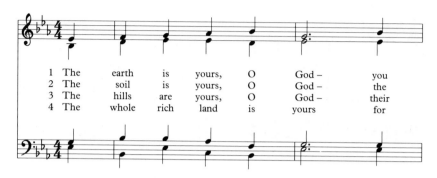

1 The earth is yours, O God – you
2 The soil is yours, O God – the
3 The hills are yours, O God – their
4 The whole rich land is yours for

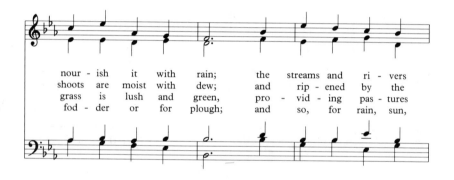

nour - ish it with rain; the streams and ri - vers
shoots are moist with dew; and rip - ened by the
grass is lush and green, pro - vid - ing pas - tures
fod - der or for plough; and so, for rain, sun,

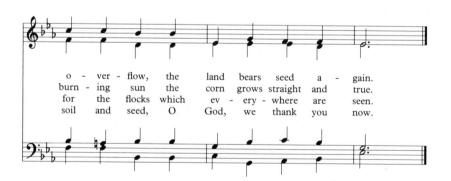

o - ver - flow, the land bears seed a - gain.
burn - ing sun the corn grows straight and true.
for the flocks which ev - ery - where are seen.
soil and seed, O God, we thank you now.

Alternative tunes: Rossleigh, St Michael

Words: from Psalm 65, Michael Saward
Music: *Harmonischer Liederschatz* (1738)

Franconia
6 6 8 6 (SM)

Ring out the bells

Unison

1 Ring out the bells and let the peo - ple know that
2 Ring out the bells and let the peo - ple hear – let
3 Ring out the bells and let the peo - ple sing through
4 Ring out the bells un - til that glo - rious day when

God is wor-shiped by the church be - low:
hearts be o - pen now, and faith draw near;
chang - ing sea - sons to our change - less King:
death shall die and sin be done a - way:

to all a - round this truth the bells de - clare –
re - ceive the grace that on - ly God can give –
all per - fect gifts are sent us from a - bove –
then comes our God so ev - ery - one shall see –

'Your needs are lift - ed up to God in prayer!'
by word and sym - bol feed and grow and live.
res - pond with prais - es for such faith - ful love.
let all the bells ring out in vic - to - ry!

Alternative tune: Woodlands

Words: Michael Perry
Music: John Barnard

Yanworth
10 10 10 10

93

By rivers of sorrow

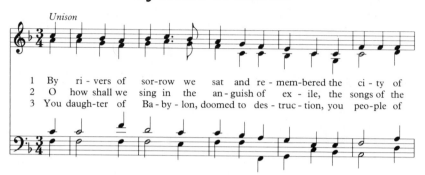

1 By ri-vers of sor-row we sat and re-mem-bered the ci-ty of
2 O how shall we sing in the an-guish of ex - ile, the songs of the
3 You daugh-ter of Ba - by - lon, doomed to des - truc-tion, you peo-ple of

hap-pi-ness where we be-long; our harps and our me - lo - dies
Lord in a far a - way land? Je - ru - sa-lem, see if I
E - dom who throw down our walls, be warned of the judge-ment on

hung in the branch-es, and there our tor - men-tors de - mand-ed a song!
ev - er for - get you till death take my voice and the skill of my hand!
you and your child - ren when blas-phe-my fails and when ty - ran-ny falls.

Words: from Psalms 137 and 138, Michael Perry

Music: American traditional melody, arranged by Noël Tredinnick and David Iliff

Streets of Laredo
12 11 12 11

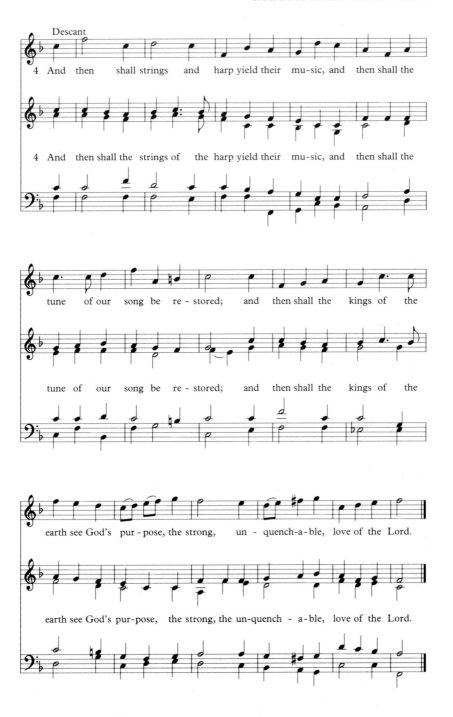

Descant

4 And then shall strings and harp yield their mu-sic, and then shall the

4 And then shall the strings of the harp yield their mu-sic, and then shall the

tune of our song be re-stored; and then shall the kings of the

tune of our song be re-stored; and then shall the kings of the

earth see God's pur-pose, the strong, un-quench-a-ble, love of the Lord.

earth see God's pur-pose, the strong, the un-quench-a-ble, love of the Lord.

Metrical index

Tune name index

Authors, composers and sources index

Numbers in italics indicate originators of texts or arrangers of tunes

American melody – 93
Amps, William (1824–1910) – 77
Avery, Colin – 80
Barnaby, Joseph (1838–1896) – 35
Barnard, John – *11, 13, 14, 15, 18, 24, 29,* 33, *44,* 56, 64, *65, 67, 69,* 75, 76, 79, 92
Baughen, Michael Alfred – 25, 58, 63, 65
Beasley, Pearl – 10
Beckley, Simon – 56
Black, Brian – 51
Bowater, Christopher A – 66
Calkin, John Baptiste (1827–1905) – 55
Coates, Kenneth Will – 72
Coates, Stephen – *19*
Cunningham, Tom – *17,* 20
Davies, Judy – 31
Dudley-Smith, Timothy – 5, 7, 40, 57, 63, 87
Edwards, Paul Christison – 16, 23, 42, 47, 60, 68
English melody – 2, 21, 22, 38, 46, 71
Fléchier, E (1632–1710) – 11
French melody – 17, 31, 89
Gauntlett, Henry John (1805–1876) – 36, 75
Gerhardt, Paul (1607–1676) – 9
German melody – 29, 90, 91
Handel, George Frideric (1685–1759) – 73
Harrison, Ralph (1748–1810) – 34
Hatton, J (died 1793) – 74
Hoare, Brian Richard – 7, 10, 26, 53
Holst, Gustav Theodore (1874–1934) – 54
Horsfall, Stephen – 65
Hughes, Beth – 15
Hundert Arien, Dresden (1694) – 70
Idle, Christopher Martin – 4, 28, 29, 44, 45, 49, 50, 55, 60, 61, 67, 70, 71, 75, 89
Iliff, David – *2, 21, 22, 31, 38, 46,* 48, *50,* 65, 83, *93*
Jones, Joseph David (1827–1870) – 27
Llewellyn Green, David – 37
Luther, Martin (1483–1546) – 84, 85

Manwaring, Randle – 82
Maries, Andrew – 52
Mowbray, David – 2, 32, 36, 47, 62, 73
Paris Antiphoner (1681) – 89
Parry, Charles Hubert Hastings (1848–1918) – 88
Peacock, David – 9, 32, *41,* 61
Perry, Michael Arnold – 1, 3, 6, 11, 12, 13, 14, 16, 19, 20, 21, 22, 30, 33, 35, 37, 38, 39, 43, 46, 54, 56, 59, 66, 80, 81, 83, 84, 85, 86, 88, 90, 92, 93
Porteous, Christopher – 15, 52
Praetorius, Michael (1571–1621) – 50
Preston, David George – 48
Sanderson, David – 12
Saward, Michael John – 8, 27, 58, 64, 69, 72, 74, 91
Schulz, Johann Abraham P (1747–1800) – 18
Seddon, James Edward – (1915–1983) – 24, 34, 41, 76, 77, 78, 79
Silesian Folk Songs, Leipzig (1842) – 90
Southern Harmony – 44
Stainer, John (1840–1901) – 45
Steggall, Charles (1826–1905) – 62
Strover, Martin Christian Tinne – 87
Sullivan, Arthur Seymour (1842–1900) – 78
Tiddeman, Maria (1837–1915) – 4
Tochter Zion, Cologne (1741) – 39
Traditional melody – *41,* 67
Tredinnick, Noël Harwood – 25, 43, *57, 58, 63, 71,* 82, *93*
Warren, Norman Leonard – 1, 3, 6, 8, 28, 40, 49, 51, 59, 69
Webbe, Samuel (the elder) (1740–1816) – 81
Welsh traditional melody – 13, 14
White, Peter Gilbert – 5, 30, 86
Wigmore, Paul – 17, 18, 23, 68
Wilson, David Gordon – 24, 57
Winkworth, Catherine (1827–1878) – 9
Woollett, Barbara – 42

Topical index

Alphabetical index of hymns